Skills Builders

Grammar and Punctuation

YEAR
2

Maddy Barnes

RISING★STARS

Rising Stars UK Ltd, 7 Hatchers Mews, Bermondsey Street, London SE1 3GS
www.risingstars-uk.com

Published 2013
Text, design and layout © 2013 Rising Stars UK Ltd

Project manager: Dawn Booth
Editorial: Sue Walton
Proofreader: Margaret Crowther
Design: Words & Pictures Ltd, London
Cover design: Amina Dudhia
Acknowledgements: p.6 iStock/Dzhamiliya Ermakova ; p.8 iStock/Milorad Zaric;
p.10 iStock/Pei Ling Wu; p.12 iStock/Ryan Burke; p.14 iStock/lilybanerjee;
p.16 iStock/Armagan Ucok Gonenc; p.17 iStock/Benoit Chartron;
p.17 iStock/Frank Ramspott; p.18 iStock/Eneri LLC; p.19 iStock/nadejda ciob;
p.20 iStock/artvea; p.21 iStock/CandO_Designs; p.21 iStock/olegtoka;
p.22 (top) iStock/ssstep; p.22 (bottom) iStock/Smokeyjo; p.23 iStock/Dusan Pavlic;
p.24 iStock/Ming Lok Fung; 20358917; p.26 iStock/Joe Peragino;
p.26 iStock/Cruz Puga; p.27 iStock/Christopher Gregory; p.28 iStock/Alias-Ching;
p.29 iStock/Kenn Wislander; p.31 iStock/dues; p.32 iStock/excape25;
p.33 iStock/Scott Wilson; p.35 Dave Thompson; p.36 iStock/viviyan;
p.37 iStock/Mark Stay; p.38 iStock/FanFan30; p.39 iStock/Miroslaw Piepryzk;
p.41 iStock/deystudio; p.41 iStock/Oleksiy Tsuper; p.42 iStock/Lorelyn Medina

British Library Cataloguing-in-Publication Data
A CIP record for this book is available from the British Library.

ISBN: 978-0-85769-693-9
Printed in Singapore by Craft Print International

Skills Builder: Grammar and Punctuation

YEAR 2

Contents

* Areas of learning pupils should have covered in Year 1.

How to use this book

What we have included:

1 Each unit covers aspects of grammar and punctuation taken from the new National Curriculum framework.

2 The units at the beginning of the book focus on basic skills which pupils should recognise from their previous learning and set mini challenges to encourage pupils to recap what they already know. These are often 'Warming up' questions, which are also used to test just learned knowledge throughout the book.

3 Other sections introduce new skills which are organised in a 'Getting hotter' section and some push even further in the 'Burn it up!' section.

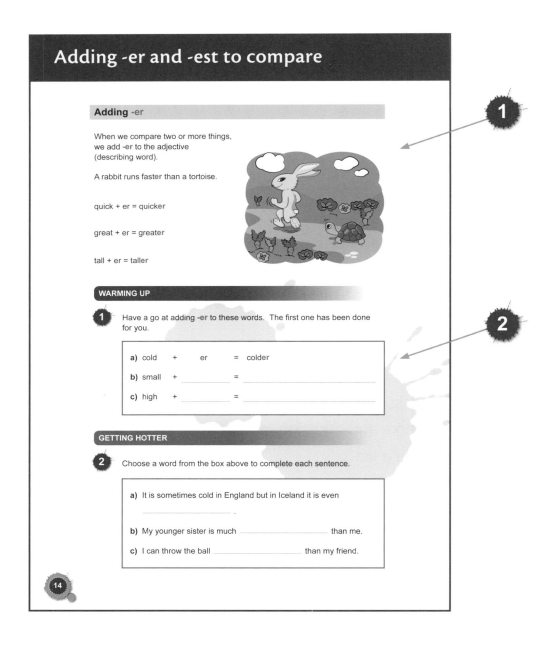

Adding -er and -est to compare

Adding -er

When we compare two or more things, we add **-er** to the adjective (describing word).

A rabbit runs faster than a tortoise.

quick + er = quicker

great + er = greater

tall + er = taller

1

WARMING UP

1 Have a go at adding **-er** to these words. The first one has been done for you.

a) cold   +   er   =   colder

b) small   +   _____   =   _____

c) high   +   _____   =   _____

2

GETTING HOTTER

2 Choose a word from the box above to complete each sentence.

a) It is sometimes cold in England but in Iceland it is even _____ .

b) My younger sister is much _____ than me.

c) I can throw the ball _____ than my friend.

14

4

How to use this book

4 At the end of each section is a 'How did I do?' assessment for learning where pupils can record how well they did.

5 There are assessment points throughout the book titled 'Assess and review', which allow opportunities for pupils to recap new learning in small steps.

6 The correct grammatical terminology is used throughout this book to encourage acquisition of technical language.

7 All answers are included so pupils can check on their progress.

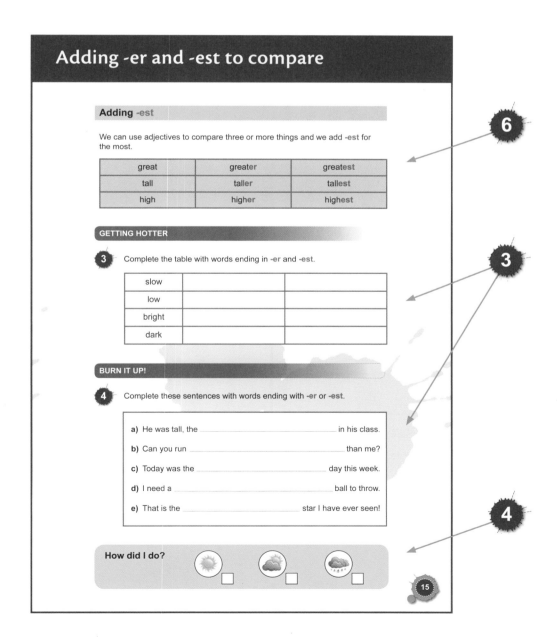

Adding -er and -est to compare

Adding -est

We can use adjectives to compare three or more things and we add -est for the most.

great	greater	greatest
tall	taller	tallest
high	higher	highest

GETTING HOTTER

3 Complete the table with words ending in -er and -est.

slow		
low		
bright		
dark		

BURN IT UP!

4 Complete these sentences with words ending with -er or -est.

a) He was tall, the _____ in his class.

b) Can you run _____ than me?

c) Today was the _____ day this week.

d) I need a _____ ball to throw.

e) That is the _____ star I have ever seen!

How did I do?

15

How un- changes the meaning of words

When we add **un-** to words (verbs and adjectives) it changes what the words mean.

Read these words:

kind	**un**kind		able	**un**able
tidy	**un**tidy		lucky	**un**lucky

Adding **un-** to a word means the word has the opposite meaning. **Un**happy is the opposite of happy.

 1 Complete the table below to create pairs of words with opposite meanings. The first pair has been done for you.

tie	untie
well	
	unofficial
usual	
	unzip
pick	
	undo
seen	
	unpopular

How did I do?

Using capital letters for names

We always write names of people or places with a capital letter. Names of people and places are nouns.

1   **a)** Circle the words in this box which should have a capital letter.

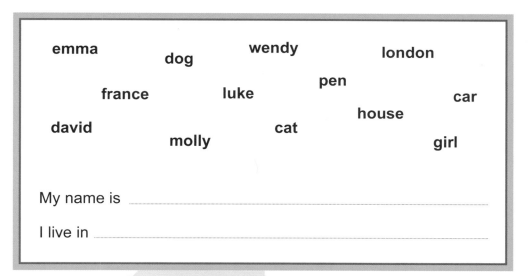

emma   dog   wendy   london

france   luke   pen   car

david   molly   cat   house   girl

My name is _____

I live in _____

b) Write your name and the place you live in the box above.

2   There are some mistakes in these names.
Write down whether each is correct or incorrect.

   a) Atlantic ocean _____

   b) tom and Sarah _____

   c) North America _____

   d) mario and joe _____

   e) Manchester _____

How did I do?   ☐   ☐   ☐

7

Using and to join words and sentences

We can use the word **and** to join words and to join two sentences.

fish **and** chips

I went to the park. I played on the swings.

I went to the park **and** played on the swings.

WARMING UP

 1 Choose two words from the box to join with the word **and**. Use different words each time.

> pen   fork   bucket
>   spade   pencil   knife

a) .... and ....

b) .... and ....

c) .... and ....

GETTING HOTTER

 2 Write another sentence so that there are two sentences joined by the word **and**.

a) He went to the beach and ....

b) She bought bread and ....

c) Mark played football and ....

How did I do?

 ☐   ☐   ☐

Assess and review

1 Here are some sentences where the words have been mixed up. Read the words carefully and use them to create a sentence that makes sense.

a)

name My Tom. is

....

....

....

b)

had Holly great a day.

....

....

....

c)

likes dancing art. and Max

....

....

....

d)

Ben and love swimming. Tim

....

....

....

GETTING HOTTER

2 Read these words which contain the prefix **-un**. Tick the words that are real ones and put a cross next to the ones that are made up.

unhappy	untidy	uncake ....
unreal	unhouse	undress ....
untable	undo	undon't ....
unfield		

How did I do? ☐ ☐ ☐

9

Adding the suffix -ness

- A **suffix** is a group of letters we add to the end of a word.
- Suffixes change the meaning or the purpose of the word.

The suffix -ness

The doctor was kind.

The doctor showed great kind**ness**.

WARMING UP

1 Add **-ness** to these words. The first one has been done for you.

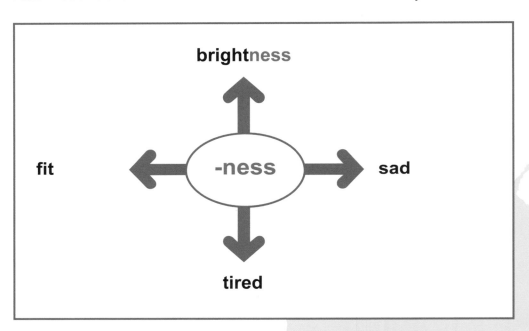

2 Choose a word from the box above to complete each sentence.
The first one has been done for you.

a) She had a pain in her leg, a headache and extreme **tiredness**.

b) The _____ centre had a swimming pool and tennis courts.

c) Our teacher changed the _____ of the bulb.

d) Happiness is the opposite of _____ .

Adding the suffix -ness

 3 Add **-ness** to these words. The first one has been done for you.

a) fair　　　+　　ness　　= fair**ness**

b) wicked　+　.................　= ....

c) foolish　+　.................　= ....

d) careless　+　.................　= ....

 4 There are four words in the box below which make nouns when you add **-ness** to them. Find them, add **-ness** and then write them down. One has been done for you.

rude　　　play　　　　forgive
joy　　　　　　great
bike
tree
door　　　　good　　　joke

forgive**ness**

a) ....

b) ....

c) ....

How did I do?

 ☐　 ☐　 ☐

11

Adding the suffix -ful

Nouns are the names of people, places, ideas, objects or things.

Adjectives describe nouns.

We can change a noun to an adjective by adding **-ful**.

When we add full to a word, we drop an l and add **-ful**.

WARMING UP

 1   Add **-ful** to these words. The first one has been done for you.

    a) care   +   ful   =   care**ful**

    b) thought   + ...   = ...

    c) wonder   + ...   = ...

GETTING HOTTER

 2   Read the sentences below, add **-ful** to the word in brackets and write the new word.

    a) Gemma was very (**cheer**).......................... at the party.

    b) My kitten is very (**play**) ....

    c) I think a dictionary is very (**use**) ....

    d) I love my new (**colour**) .... dress.

    e) I cut my leg and it is very (**pain**) ....

    f) Mum said I could have a (**hand**) .... of sweets from the bowl.

    g) Dad's new lawnmower is very (**power**)

    ....

How did I do?

 ☐   ☐   ☐

Adding the suffix -ment

We can add the suffix **-ment** to change a verb (an action) to a noun (the name of a person, place, idea, object or thing).

Frankie likes to entertain the class.

Her jokes are great entertain**ment**.

entertain + ment = entertain**ment**

WARMING UP

 1 Add **-ment** to the following verbs to create nouns. The first has been done for you.

a) appoint   +   ment   =   appoint**ment**

b) depart   + ...   = ...

c) treat   + ...   = ...

GETTING HOTTER

2 Match the pairs of words. One has been done for you.

move	punishment
excite	agreement
punish	improvement
equip	movement
agree	excitement
improve	equipment

How did I do?   ☐   ☐   ☐

Adding -er and -est to compare

Adding -er

When we compare two or more things, we add **-er** to the adjective (describing word).

A rabbit runs fast**er** than a tortoise.

quick + er = quick**er**

great + er = great**er**

tall + er = tall**er**

WARMING UP

1 Have a go at adding **-er** to these words. The first one has been done for you.

> **a)** cold + er = cold**er**
>
> **b)** small + ... = ...
>
> **c)** high + ... = ...

GETTING HOTTER

2 Choose a word from the box above to complete each sentence.

> **a)** It is sometimes cold in England but in Iceland it is even
>
> ....
>
> **b)** My younger sister is much .... than me.
>
> **c)** I can throw the ball .... than my friend.

14

Adding -er and -est to compare

Adding -est

We can use adjectives to compare three or more things and we add **-est** for the most.

great	great**er**	great**est**
tall	tall**er**	tall**est**
high	high**er**	high**est**

GETTING HOTTER

 3   Complete the table with words ending in **-er** and **-est**.

slow		
low		
bright		
dark		

BURN IT UP!

4   Complete these sentences with words ending with **-er** or **-est**.

a) He was tall, the .... in his class.

b) Can you run .... than me?

c) Today was the .... day this week.

d) I need a .... ball to throw.

e) That is the .... star I have ever seen!

How did I do?

 ☐   ☐   ☐

Using because and if

Using because

We use the word **because** to join two sentences. The second sentence explains the first sentence.

> The girl went to bed **because** she was tired.
>
> The boy ate the cake **because** he was hungry.
>
> The boy ate the cake **because** it was his birthday.

WARMING UP

 1   Think of a reason to add to each of these sentences.

a) Mum picked up the baby because ....

....

....

b) Dad went to the shop because ....

....

....

c) I wore my coat and hat because ....

....

....

d) The squirrel climbed the tree because ....

....

....

Using because and if

Using if

We use the word **if** to connect two sentences. The second sentence depends on the first sentence.

You can play outside today **if** it is sunny.

We will go to the park after school **if** there is time.

GETTING HOTTER

2 Add a reason after **if** so that each sentence makes sense.

a) I will take my umbrella if ....

b) Mum will buy you a new toy if ....

BURN IT UP!

3 Complete each sentence with **because** or **if**.

a) Dad bought a new TV .... the old one broke.

b) Your teacher will be happy .... you do your homework.

c) You will be tired .... you do not go to bed.

d) Kirsty had a drink .... she was thirsty.

How did I do?

 ☐   ☐   ☐

Using or as a connective

We use the word **or** to offer a choice in a sentence.

Would you like an apple **or** an orange?

She could be very kind **or** really mean.

WARMING UP

 1 Underline the sentences that do not make sense.

a) I could have a bath or a shower.

b) I want to play out or it is too windy.

c) Can I have pasta or pizza for lunch please?

d) Martin likes playing football or he is very good at it.

e) Apples are usually red or green.

GETTING HOTTER

2 Write a sentence of your own using **or** as a connective.

How did I do?

Using but as a connective

We use **but** to join two sentences. Usually there is something surprising in the second sentence which is connected to the first sentence.

Jamie wanted to draw a picture **but** he didn't have any paper.

I was supposed to go on holiday this morning **but** I missed the train.

WARMING UP

 1 Complete each of the sentences below by adding a second sentence after but.

a) I really want to watch TV but ....

....

....

b) My teacher is really kind but ....

....

....

c) Nicola's best friend is Hayley but ....

....

....

How did I do?

 ☐ ☐ ☐

Creating expanded noun phrases

Revise

A noun is the name of:

> ✓ **a person**
>
> ✓ **a place**
>
> ✓ **an animal**
>
> ✓ **a thing**

This is a car. But if we were describing this car to a person who had not seen it we would need to say more than just **the car**. We would need to expand our sentence.

What could we say?

red	sporty	shiny	cool	amazing

the car

the red car

the sporty red car

the sporty, shiny red car

The sporty, shiny red car is cool and amazing.

We have used more words to add detail and description. Our sentence is longer and the car sounds much more interesting too.

Creating expanded noun phrases

the cat

Here are some words to describe the cat:

stripy	brown	cute	playful

 Choose words to write four sentences about the cat using expanded noun phrases.

a) ....

b) ....

c) ....

d) ....

GETTING HOTTER

 Here is a pizza. How can we describe it?

		tasty		

BURN IT UP!

 Write three sentences about the pizza – don't forget to expand each one.

a) ....

b) ....

c) ....

How did I do?

 ☐   ☐   ☐

Tenses – present and past

Verbs can be written in the present or the past tense.

The **present tense** is something that is happening now.

The **past tense** shows something that has already happened.

Verb: to walk

The man **walks** to work.

Yesterday the man **walked** to work.

Verb	Present	Past
to think	thinking	thought
to listen	listening	listened
to jump	jumping	jumped

WARMING UP

1 Try to complete the table below.

Verb	Present	Past
to run		
to wash		

Answers

Skills Builders

Grammar and Punctuation

YEAR
2

Maddy Barnes

How un- changes the meaning of words (page 6)

1

well	unwell
official	unofficial
usual	unusual
zip	unzip
pick	unpick
do	undo
seen	unseen
popular	unpopular

Using capital letters for names (page 7)

1 a) (Emma) (France) (Wendy) (Luke) (London) (David) (Molly)

b) Answers will vary

2 a) incorrect **b)** incorrect **c)** correct **d)** incorrect **e)** correct

Using and to join words and sentences (page 8)

1 Order of answers will vary

a) pen and pencil **b)** bucket and spade **c)** knife and fork

2 Answers will vary

a) swam in the sea.

b) made sandwiches for us all.

c) his team won.

Assess and review (page 9)

1 a) My name is Tom.

b) Holly had a great day.

c) Max likes dancing and art.

d) Ben and Tim love swimming.

2 Tick: unhappy, unreal, undo, untidy, undress

Cross: undon't, uncake, unhouse, unfield, untable

Adding the suffix -ness (pages 10–11)

1 sadness, tiredness, fitness

2 b) The **fitness** centre had a swimming pool and tennis courts.

c) Our teacher changed the **brightness** of the bulb.

d) Happiness is the opposite of **sadness**.

3 b) wickedness **c)** foolishness **d)** carelessness

4 a) rudeness **b)** greatness **c)** goodness (order may vary)

Adding the suffix -ful (page 12)

1 b) thoughtful **c)** wonderful

2 a) cheerful **b)** playful **c)** useful **d)** colourful **e)** painful **f)** handful

g) powerful

Adding the suffix -ment (page 13)

1 b) department **c)** treatment

2

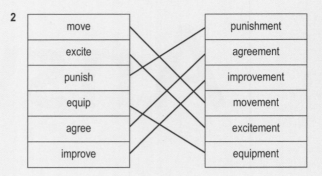

Adding -er and -est to compare (pages 14–15)

1 b) smaller **c)** higher

2 a) It is sometimes cold in England but in Iceland it is even **colder**.

b) My younger sister is much **smaller** than me.

c) I can throw the ball **higher** than my friend.

3

slow	slower	slowest
low	lower	lowest
bright	brighter	brightest
dark	darker	darkest

4 Answers will vary

a) tallest **b)** faster **c)** coldest / hottest **d)** bigger / smaller **e)** brightest

Using because and if (pages 16–17)

1 Answers will vary

a) he was crying. **b)** we needed more bread. **c)** it was freezing cold.

d) the cat was chasing him.

2 Answers will vary

a) it looks like rain. **b)** you are a good girl.

3 a) because **b)** if **c)** if **d)** because

Using or as a connective (page 18)

1 b and d underlined

2 Answers will vary

I will go for a walk now or maybe I will go later.

Using but as a connective (page 19)

1 Answers will vary

a) I must complete my homework first.

b) she still makes me work hard.

c) Nicola is not Hayley's best friend.

Creating expanded noun phrases (page 21)

1 Answers will vary

a) The cat is very playful.

b) My cat is so cute when he curls up in a ball.

c) This cat has a stripy brown coat.

d) The brown cat is sitting down.

2 Answers will vary

round	crusty	tasty	hot	meaty

3 Answers will vary

a) This pizza is very crusty.

b) This pizza is eaten when it is hot.

c) The pizza is very tasty because it is meaty.

Tenses – present and past (pages 22–23)

1

Verb	Present	Past
to run	running	ran
to wash	washing	washed

2 a) I saw a bright flower. b) The boy played football.

c) The girl drank her milk.

3

Present tense	Past tense
happening now	**it has already happened**
singing, drawing, fixing, reading	hopped, swam, ate, ran, broke, brushed, slept

Practise adding -ing and -ed to verbs (page 24)

1

talked	talk	talking
helped	help	helping
opened	open	opening

2 a) Yesterday I (opening) the presents.

b) Today I (walk) to the park with my friends.

c) I (wanting) to pick a flower for my Grandad.

d) I like (helped) my teacher at school.

e) I was (played) with Billy in the park.

Adding -s or -es when making nouns plural (page 25)

1

pencil	pencils
day	days

boy	boys
book	books
flower	flowers

2

fox	foxes
table	tables
cup	cups
bush	bushes

bird	birds
torch	torches
wish	wishes
tree	trees

Verbs in the present tense (page 26)

1 Answers will vary

a) I am drinking a cup of tea. She is drinking a cup of tea.

b) They are making a cake. I am making a cake.

c) I am playing the clarinet. He is playing the clarinet.

d) She is writing a letter. I am writing a letter.

Verbs in the past tense (page 27)

2 Answers will vary

a) By 8.30 p.m. I was sleeping.

b) From 12 p.m.–1 p.m. I was eating lunch.

c) At 8.30 a.m. I was walking to school.

d) I was swimming between 3 p.m.–5 p.m.

Assess and review (pages 28–29)

1 Answers will vary

new, fine, white, blue, crispy, thick, tasty, cold, large, noisy, tiny

2 Answers will vary

a) What is your name?

b) When did you move to London?

c) Do you like playing football?

d) Have you got any pets?

3

They looked for their dog	and	a magazine?
You can go to the cinema	or	swimming.
I like football	but	it is very hot.
Would you like to read a book	because	you are good.
He is wearing suncream	if	they could not find him.

4 a) because b) but c) so d) and

Proper nouns – using capital letters (pages 30–31)

1 Answers will vary

Names of people	Names of days	Names of countries	Names of months
Roanne	Monday	Switzerland	January
Kelly	Wednesday	France	May
Imran	Saturday	Italy	June
Iona	Tuesday	Thailand	December

2 a) Mr Dickinson is a brilliant maths teacher.

b) The train took three hours to travel from Manchester to London.

3 a) Yesterday <u>i</u> went to <u>c</u>hester <u>z</u>oo.

  b) Stephen and <u>p</u>aul are brothers.

  c) <u>d</u>o you want a biscuit?

  d) Wednesday is the day after <u>t</u>uesday.

  e) London is the capital of England.

Using full stops accurately (pages 32–33)

1 a) Today is hot and sunny.

  b) My favourite dessert is ice cream.

2 It was not an ordinary day for **B**en. He had waited all week for it. Monday, **T**uesday and **W**ednesday had passed and at last it was Thursday. **B**en could finally celebrate his birthday. Mum and dad had promised to take **B**en to his favourite place – the safari park. **B**en was hoping to see monkeys, lions and tigers. **B**en jumped out of bed, ran down the stairs and flung open the kitchen door. "Wow, Happy Birthday **B**en," sang his family.

Statements, questions and exclamations (page 35)

1 a) The cute kitten sat on the step.

  b) What time did you wake up?

  c) Stop!

  d) What a lovely day. or !

  e) The girls cycled to the park on their bikes.

  f) Can you see the helicopter in the sky?

2 a) S b) E c) Q

3. Answers will vary

Statement .	Question ?	Exclamation !
The monkey is hiding behind a tree.	What is the animal with a trunk?	The giant is very tall!
There are lots of leaves on the ground.	What is the animal with horns on its head?	"Mind out snake!"

Exclamation marks and question marks (page 37)

1 a) Have you got your coat?

  b) Do you know where my phone is?

  c) What a brilliant joke!

  d) Give me that cake!

  e) Can I borrow a pencil please?

2 a) Kirsty bought a dress, shoes and a hat.

  b) Did you hear what he said?

  c) Faye worked her socks off at school.

  d) The rabbit searched for his burrow.

  e) How did you manage to do that?

  f) Don't you dare take that biscuit!

Using commas in a list (pages 38–39)

1 a) I had pizza, chips and beans for lunch.

  b) Laura needs a pencil, rubber and ruler.

  c) Daniel wore his hat, scarf and gloves today.

  d) I love pink, yellow and purple flowers.

  e) Raj loves playing football,rugby and rounders.

  f) Hattie had an apple, a sandwich and a drink in her lunch box.

  g) Amber danced, sang and told jokes in the talent competition.

2 Any order is acceptable

  a) Granny had wool, knitting needles and scissors in her bag.

  b) The wizard had a wand, cloak, cards and rabbits in his bag.

  c) The teacher has pens, pencils, books and sweets in her bag.

  d) I have sweets, books, pencils and pens in my bag.

Using apostrophes accurately (pages 40–42)

1 it is / it's; do not / don't; I will / I'll; should have / should've

2

the door	handle	the door's handle
the desk	chair	the desk's chair
the boat	engine	the boat's engine

3 Answers will vary

The dog's wearing a collar.

The dog's tongue is pink.

The dog's tail is curly.

4 a) I'm fine, thank you.

  b) Tomorrow we'll go swimming.

  c) I have tried but I really can't do it.

  d) If I don't do my homework I will be in trouble.

Assess and review (page 43)

1 a) Faye woke up and put on her slippers, dressing gown and hairband.

  b) "Would you like to go to the cinema?" asked Mum.

  c) Today has been an amazing and fantastic day, probably the best day in the whole world!

  d) I went to the shop and bought crisps, popcorn and chocolate for the party.

  e) Don't you want to play with the other children?

  f) The girl's bag was on the floor and she could not find it.

  g) "Hey, stop that right now!"

  h) Jackie had a pen, ruler, pencil and calculator in her school bag.

  i) Ben loves playing with Sean, Sam, Kevin and Tim.

  j) I can't believe I got all of the answers right!

2 Can you change these sentences to the past tense?

I am walking to school.

I walked to school.

a) I can see a bright flower.

....

b) The boy is playing football.

....

c) The girl is drinking her milk.

....

BURN IT UP!

3 Read these verbs and decide if they are in the present tense or the past tense. Write them in the table in the correct column.

hopped	swam	singing	drawing	ate	ran
broke	fixing	reading	brushed	slept	

Present tense	Past tense
happening now	it has already happened

How did I do?

 ☐   ☐   ☐

23

Practise adding -ing and -ed to verbs

Verbs are words which describe what we do such as to run, climb or eat.

Play	Walk
I am play**ing** Yesterday I play**ed**	I am walk**ing** Yesterday I walk**ed**

WARMING UP

1 Can you complete each verb form for the past and present tense?

pick**ed**	pick	pick**ing**
	talk	
	help	
	open	

GETTING HOTTER

2 Circle the mistakes in these sentences.

a) Yesterday I opening the presents.

b) Today I walk to the park with my friends.

c) I wanting to pick a flower for my Grandad.

d) I like helped my teacher at school.

e) I was played with Billy in the park.

How did I do?

24

Adding -s or -es when making nouns plural

A noun is the name of a person, place, animal or thing.

For example, **dog, cat, book, girl, pen, chair, table**.

However, if we have more than one object we must change the singular to plural.

1 pen **2 pens**   **1 girl** **5 girls**

1 Change these nouns from singular to plural:

cat	cats		boy	
pencil			book	
day			flower	

If the noun ends with **-s**, **-ch**, **-sh**, **-x** or **-z** then we add **-es**. For example:

1 box **4 boxes**   **1 watch** **10 watches**

GETTING HOTTER

2 Use the rules above to change these singular nouns to plural nouns.

fox			bird	
table			torch	
cup			wish	
bush			tree	

How did I do?

25

Verbs in the present tense

The continuous form of the present tense means what you are doing right now.
It is made with the present form of the verb **to be** + the **-ing** form of the verb.

What is he doing?

He **is drawing** a picture.

What are they doing?

They **are playing** football.

WARMING UP

 1 Choose a pronoun from the blue text and an activity from the red text and write four sentences to show what they are doing.

I	making a cake
they	playing the clarinet
he	writing a letter
she	drinking a cup of tea

For example:

He **is writing** a letter.

a) ....

b) ....

c) ....

d) ....

How did I do?

 ☐   ☐   ☐

Verbs in the past tense

The continuous form of the past tense means what you were doing. It is made using the past form of the verb **to be**, **was** or **were**, with the **-ing** form of the verb.

This is an example of the past tense:

Yesterday Annie **played** basketball.

This is an example of the continuous form of the past tense:

Annie **was playing** basketball yesterday.

What did you do yesterday?

7.30 a.m.	eating breakfast
8.30 a.m.	walking to school
9 a.m.–12 p.m.	in lessons
12 p.m.–1 p.m.	eating lunch
3 p.m.–5 p.m.	swimming
7 p.m.	eating dinner
8.30 p.m.	sleeping

WARMING UP

 1 Use the table above to write some sentences about what you did yesterday using the continuous form of the past tense.

➤ At 7 p.m. I was eating my dinner.

➤ From 9 a.m. until 12 p.m. I was having lessons.

a) ....

b) ....

c) ....

d) ....

How did I do?

27

Assess and review

1 Read the paragraph below and add some adjectives (describing words) to add more detail.

> James had a .... bike which he loved. One .... morning
>
> he decided to go to the park. He wore his .... t-shirt and his
>
> .... shorts. James took a tasty lunch with him in his lunch box.
>
> He packed a .... apple, a .... and
>
> .... sandwich and a .... drink. On the
>
> way to the park he cycled past a .... and
>
> .... dog, a shiny blue sports car and a
>
> .... kitten that was stuck up a tree.

GETTING HOTTER

2 Imagine there is a new child in your school and you want to ask them some questions. Use these question openers to write some questions to ask your new classmate. **Don't forget to use a question mark at the end.**

a) What ....

....

b) When ....

....

c) Do ....

....

d) Have ....

....

Assess and review

 3 Choose and colour an opener, a connective and an ending to make a sentence. One has been done for you.

They looked for their dog	and	a magazine?
You can go to the cinema	or	swimming.
I like football	but	it is very hot.
Would you like to read a book	because	you are good.
He is wearing suncream	if	they could not find him.

 4 Choose a connective to complete each sentence.

because	and	but	so

a) Nadien put on his coat _____ it was raining.

b) I would like to buy a new book _____ I haven't got any money.

c) Sarah was hungry _____ she made a sandwich to eat.

d) Yesterday I cycled to the lake _____ began fishing.

How did I do? ☐ ☐ ☐

Proper nouns – using capital letters

A	B	C	D	E	F	G	H	I	J	K	L	M
a	b	c	d	e	f	g	h	i	j	k	l	m
N	O	P	Q	R	S	T	U	V	W	X	Y	Z
n	o	p	q	r	s	t	u	v	w	x	y	z

Capital letters are used for

➤ names of people, nationalities, languages, countries, places, days, months (proper nouns)

➤ to start a sentence

➤ the personal pronoun I.

WARMING UP

 1 Add five more proper nouns to each column in the table.

Names of people	Names of days	Names of countries	Names of months
Angela	Friday	China	November
Michael	Tuesday	Ireland	April

Proper nouns – using capital letters

GETTING HOTTER

2 Write these sentences using capital letters correctly.

a) mr dickinson is a brilliant maths teacher.

....

....

b) the train took three hours to travel from manchester to london.

....

....

When we write about ourselves, we always use a capital I.

| I ran. | I am hungry. | It is sunny and I am hot. |

BURN IT UP!

3 Read these sentences and check if the capital letters are used correctly. Underline the places where there are mistakes.

a) Yesterday i went to chester zoo.

b) Stephen and paul are brothers.

c) do you want a biscuit?

d) Wednesday is the day after tuesday.

e) London is the capital of England.

How did I do?

Using full stops accurately

A sentence

> ✓ **starts with a capital letter**
> ✓ **ends with a full stop**
> ✓ **makes complete sense.**

A **full stop** shows the end of a sentence or statement.

A sentence only needs one **full stop**.

The dog is in the kennel.

The kennel is made from wood.

The dog is called Lucky.

WARMING UP

1 Use the words in each box to make a sentence. Add the full stop at the end.

a)

is	hot	sunny	Today	and

b)

dessert	is	my	ice cream	favourite

Using full stops accurately

2 The thief has stolen some of the capital letters and full stops.

Read the paragraph below and put the capital letters and full stops in correctly.

It was not an ordinary day for ben He had waited all week for it Monday, tuesday and wednesday had passed and at last it was Thursday ben could finally celebrate his birthday Mum and dad had promised to take ben to his favourite place – the safari park ben was hoping to see monkeys, lions and tigers ben jumped out of bed, ran down the stairs and flung open the kitchen door "Wow, Happy Birthday ben," sang his family.

How did I do?

Statements, questions and exclamations

Sentences can be

Statements	It was sunny today. I saw a big, scary dog near the post office. The train was on time.	•
Questions	Do you know him? Have you seen the film? Are you ready?	?
Exclamations	Oh dear! I cannot believe you! What an amazing picture!	!

A **statement** is a sentence which gives us information. A full stop is needed at the end of a statement.

A **question** is a sentence which seeks information. A question mark is needed at the end of a question.

An **exclamation** is a sentence which shows us that the speaker is impressed or filled with emotion about something. An exclamation mark is needed at the end of an exclamation.

Statements, questions and exclamations

 1 Read each of these sentences. Decide if the sentence is a statement, question or exclamation. When you have decided, choose the correct punctuation mark to complete the sentence.

a) The cute kitten sat on the step ⎯⎯⎯⎯

b) What time did you wake up ⎯⎯⎯⎯

c) Stop ⎯⎯⎯⎯

d) What a lovely day ⎯⎯⎯⎯

e) The girls cycled to the park on their bikes ⎯⎯⎯⎯

f) Can you see the helicopter in the sky ⎯⎯⎯⎯

.

?

!

 2 Look carefully at this picture. Label the statement **S**, the question **Q** and the exclamation **E**.

a) The bird is flying. ⎯⎯⎯⎯

b) Help! ⎯⎯⎯⎯

c) What is your name? ⎯⎯⎯⎯

3 Now use the picture to write some other sentences.

Statement **.**	Question **?**	Exclamation **!**

How did I do?

Exclamation marks and question marks

Three punctuation marks can show the end of a sentence.

.	?	!
Shows the end of a statement.	Shows the end of a question.	Shows a raised voice or strong feelings.

We ask questions when we want to find out information.

Questions sometimes begin with:

Who	What	When	Where	Why	How

However, we can also ask questions like this:

"Do you know what time it is?"

"Don't you have the key Mum?"

"Did you have a good time at the party?"

"Could you give me the ball please Luke?"

"Would you like milk or water Claire?"

Exclamation marks are used to show strong feelings.

"I can't believe my eyes!"

"Sit down at once Jackie!"

"Ready, steady, go!"

Exclamation marks and question marks

  1 Read each sentence and complete it with a question mark or exclamation mark.

a) Have you got your coat ....

b) Do you know where my phone is ....

c) What a brilliant joke ....

d) Give me that cake ....

e) Can I borrow a pencil please ....

  2 Read the sentences and complete them with a

a) Kirsty bought a dress, shoes and a hat ....

b) Did you hear what he said ....

c) Faye worked her socks off at school ....

d) The rabbit searched for his burrow ....

e) How did you manage to do that ....

f) Don't you dare take that biscuit ....

How did I do?

 ☐   ☐   ☐

Using commas in a list

When we write lists we must separate items in the list with a comma.

We could write:

> I bought milk **and** apples **and** bananas **and** biscuits.

There are too many **ands** in this sentence. To separate the items in the list we can use a comma instead of the word **and**.

> I bought milk, apples, bananas **and** biscuits.

 1 Read these sentences and add commas correctly.

a) I had pizza chips and beans for lunch.

b) Laura needs a pencil rubber and ruler.

c) Daniel wore his hat scarf and gloves today.

d) I love pink yellow and purple flowers.

e) Raj loves playing football rugby and rounders.

f) Hattie had an apple a sandwich and a drink in her lunch box.

g) Amber danced sang and told jokes in the talent competition.

Using commas in a list

2 Use the words in the tables to write sentences using commas correctly.

Granny	wool knitting needles scissors

a) Granny had ....

.... in her bag.

The wizard	wand cloak rabbits cards

b) The wizard had ....

.... in his bag.

The teacher	pens pencils books sweets

c) The teacher has ....

.... in her bag.

d) I have ....

.... in my bag.

How did I do?

 ☐   ☐   ☐

Using apostrophes accurately

Using apostrophes to shorten words

Sometimes we shorten words. When we do this we use an apostrophe to show where letters have been missed out.

cannot ➡ can't

we will ➡ we'll

you are ➡ you're

I am ➡ I'm

WARMING UP

1 Match the words and phrases that have the same meaning.

it is
do not
I will
should have

don't
I'll
should've
it's

Using apostrophes accurately

Using apostrophes to show ownership

We also use an apostrophe to show ownership.

If the coat belongs to the boy, we write:

> The boy's coat …

If we see a dog with a bone we can write:

> The dog's bone …

Here are some more examples:

> The girl's bag …
>
> The cat's blanket …
>
> The car's wheel …

GETTING HOTTER

2 Complete the table to show how an apostrophe is used for possession.

the man	hat	the man's hat
the door	handle	
the desk	chair	
the boat	engine	

Using apostrophes accurately

Remember we can use the apostrophe when

➤ letters are missed out of words
➤ to show something belongs to somebody.

3 Draw the dog in different colours.

You could trace him.

Then write three more sentences about the dog using an apostrophe in each one.

The dog's nose is black.
a)
b)
c)

4 Complete the sentences below by choosing from the following words:

can't	I'm	we'll	don't

a) _____ fine, thank you.

b) Tomorrow _____ go swimming.

c) I have tried but I really _____ do it.

d) If I _____ do my homework I will be in trouble.

How did I do?

Assess and review

1 Some of the punctuation is missing from the sentences below. Using everything you know about capital letters, full stops, commas, question marks, exclamation marks and apostrophes, fill in the gaps with the correct punctuation mark. Underline the words that should have a capital letter.

a) Faye woke up and put on her slippers .... dressing gown and hairband ....

b) "Would you like to go to the cinema .... " asked Mum.

c) Today has been an amazing and fantastic day, probably the best day in the whole world ....

d) I went to the shop and bought crisps .... popcorn and chocolate for the party ....

e) Don ...... t you want to play with the other children ....

f) The girl ...... s bag was on the floor and she could not find it ....

g) "Hey, stop that right now .... "

h) Jackie had a pen .... ruler .... pencil and calculator in her school bag.

i) Ben loves playing with sean .... sam .... kevin .... and tim.

j) i can't believe i got all of the answers right

How did I do?

 ☐ ☐ ☐

The Skills Builders Range

Grammar and Punctuation

Skills Builders
Grammar and Punctuation
YEAR 2 — Age 6–7

Skills Builders
Grammar and Punctuation
YEAR 3 — Age 7–8

Skills Builders
Grammar and Punctuation
YEAR 4 — Age 8–9

Skills Builders
Grammar and Punctuation
YEAR 5 — Age 9–10

Skills Builders
Grammar and Punctuation
YEAR 6 — Age 10–11

Spelling and Vocabulary

Skills Builders
Spelling and Vocabulary
YEAR 2 — Age 6–7

Skills Builders
Spelling and Vocabulary
YEAR 3 — Age 7–8

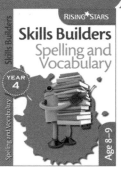
Skills Builders
Spelling and Vocabulary
YEAR 4 — Age 8–9

Skills Builders
Spelling and Vocabulary
YEAR 5 — Age 9–10

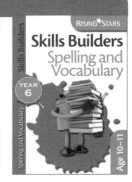
Skills Builders
Spelling and Vocabulary
YEAR 6 — Age 10–11

Times Tables

Skills Builders
Times Tables
1, 2, 5 and 10 — Book 1

Skills Builders
Times Tables
3, 4, 6 and 8 — Book 2

Skills Builders
Times Tables
7, 9, 11 and 12 — Book 3

Fractions, Decimals and Percentages

Skills Builders
Fractions, Decimals and Percentages
YEAR 3 — Age 7–8

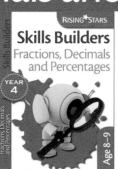
Skills Builders
Fractions, Decimals and Percentages
YEAR 4 — Age 8–9

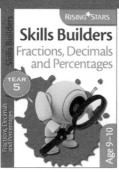
Skills Builders
Fractions, Decimals and Percentages
YEAR 5 — Age 9–10

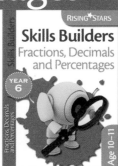
Skills Builders
Fractions, Decimals and Percentages
YEAR 6 — Age 10–11